TEENAGE MUTANT NINJA TURTLES®

A NOVELIZATION

B. B. Hiller

YEARLING BOOKS

— for Andy Hiller
and his cousin
Jonathan Stilwell

TEENAGE MUTANT NINJA TURTLES®
A YEARLING BOOK 0 440 86280 9

First published in USA by Dell Publishing

First published in Great Britain by Yearling Books
Published by arrangement with Dell Publishing, a division of Bantam
Doubleday Dell Publishing Group, Inc.

PRINTING HISTORY
Yearling edition published 1990

This book is set in 11/14 pt Baskerville by
Chippendale Type Limited, Otley, West Yorkshire.

Yearling Books are published by Transworld Publishers Ltd, 61-63
Uxbridge Road, Ealing, London W5 5SA, in Australia by Transworld
Publishers (Australia) Pty Ltd, 15-23 Helles Avenue, Moorebank,
NSW 2170, and in New Zealand by Transworld Publishers (NZ) Ltd,
Cnr Moselle and Waipareira Avenues, Henderson, Auckland.

Made and printed in Great Britain by
Cox & Wyman Ltd, Reading, Berkshire.

1

It was the worst of times. The citizens of New York were being victimized daily by a terrible crime wave. It seemed that nothing, and nobody, could – or would – stop it.

April O'Neil, crime reporter for Channel Three News, looked into the camera lens.

'Those of you who have had watches stolen from your wrists, wallets snatched from your pockets, and TVs whisked from your homes know that this is much more than just a series of small, isolated incidents. There's an organized criminal element at work, and at the moment, business is good. So good, in fact, that nobody ever sees the criminals!'

It was hard to believe, but it was true. The criminals were so skilled and so fast that nobody ever heard them coming or saw them going! People were beginning to call it an invisible, silent crime wave.

'. . . But perhaps the most disturbing silence is that coming from City Hall,' April said sternly, finishing her report.

Like a lot of citizens, April was angry that the police had got nowhere in solving the crimes. It seemed as if the police were trying to pretend that there wasn't a problem at all!

April unhooked her mike. Her work was done for the night. It was time to go home. April said goodnight to the cameraman and the guard at Channel Three. Her old Volkswagen van was in the car-park next to the Channel Three studio. As she walked through the car-park, she thought about the interview she was having with Chief Sterns the next day. She wasn't thinking about the faint tinkling of broken glass near by. She wasn't thinking about the four dark-clad men taking TV monitors from the Channel Three truck next to her van. She wasn't thinking about the video camera they removed from the front seat. She was just thinking about Chief Sterns, until the bright car-park light reflected off the blade of a razor-sharp knife – aimed at her!

'Bad timing,' one of the thieves muttered.

'You're telling me!' April said. One of the thugs grabbed her. She screamed, but the thug covered her mouth with his hand. April knew the Channel Three guard was too far away to hear her. April O'Neil, crime reporter, was afraid she was about to become another statistic in the city's crime wave!

Suddenly there was a glint of steel high above her head and the crash of broken glass. Someone, or some*thing*, had knocked out the car-park light. The whole place was pitch-black. The thug holding April released her, shoving her against her own van. April couldn't see anything, but she could hear a lot. She heard thumps, grunts, and moans. Somebody was attacking the thugs and, from the sound of things, that somebody was winning. But who could it be?

After a few minutes there was silence, then April heard the sound of police sirens. When the police arrived, they turned on their searchlights. There, in front of April, were her four attackers, all completely tied up, ready for delivery to gaol. There was no sign of whoever had beaten them and tied them up. The police looked at April for an explanation. There was none.

While the police shuffled the thugs into the patrol van, April looked around again. There was nothing to explain what happened, except ... Something shiny caught April's eye. It was a strange-looking three-pronged dagger. It was right beneath the broken car-park light, near a manhole cover. April leaned over to pick up the dagger. As she did, she thought she saw the manhole cover rise. She thought she saw a pair of eyes watching her pick up the dagger. She thought she saw something green – with a red mask! The manhole cover dropped back into place. April stepped over to it and shone a torchlight through one of the holes so she could peer through another.

At first there was only darkness. Then there was a slight motion. She squinted to see what was moving. It looked a bit, just a little bit, like the shell of a turtle!

April shook her head, trying to clear the cobwebs.

'One of those guys must have hit me pretty hard,' she said, thinking out loud. 'I'm beginning to see things!'

2

But April wasn't losing her mind, for hurrying through the sewers of the city of New York were four creatures, the very ones who had saved April from the thugs in the car-park. They *were* turtles, but they weren't *just* turtles. They were mutant, they were ninja—

'Hey, we were awesome, bros! Awesome!'

'Most excellent!'

'Outrageous!'

'Totally!'

—and they were teenagers. They called themselves Teenage Mutant Ninja Turtles.

Leonardo led the way through the dark tunnels of sewer. He wore a blue mask and carried katana – ninja fighting-swords. In the heat of battle, Leo, as his friends called him, was cool under fire. He was a natural leader, careful and disciplined.

Leo was followed by Michaelangelo, Mike to his friends, who wore an orange mask and was armed with lethal nunchukus, a ninja weapon consisting of two thick sticks joined by a chain. Mike was as easygoing and wisecracking as his weapon was fierce. When he swung the sticks in battle, it seemed that nothing could stop him.

Donatello, called Don, followed Mike through the sewer. Don was quiet and thoughtful. He had mechanical ability, too, and could fix almost anything. With his bo, a four-foot-long staff that had pointed ends, he could fix most of his enemies. Don's mask was purple.

Finally, trailing well behind his celebrating friends, was Raphael. He grumbled to himself. There was a frightening intensity to his anger. He sloshed through the muddy sewer, staring at the one sai that he had now. His other sai, or fighting dagger, was in April O'Neil's purse. He vowed to get it back.

Ahead, the door to the Turtles' home, their den, opened, spilling bright light into the dank sewer. Raph sighed at his single sai, half of a pair, and followed his brothers into their den.

The Turtles and their ninja master, an elderly human-sized rat named Splinter, lived in an abandoned sewer maintenance room. The place was furnished with odds and ends they'd found outside their door. Thanks to Don's mechanical abilities, it was quite well equipped. They had a telephone, a television, electricity, and even heat. What was most important about it, though, was that it was home.

Splinter watched as his students came through the door. Like the Turtles, he was much larger than others of his breed. He was about four feet tall. Age had withered him some. His fur was greying. His back was bent with the pain of old age. Half of his right ear was missing, a battle scar from many years ago. His eyes watched with love and wisdom.

'We have had our first battle, Master Splinter,' Leo said. He was so excited, it was almost hard for him to talk. 'There were many, but we kicked—' he stopped himself. There was something about Splinter that made him want to talk more formally than he usually did. '—I mean, we fought well.'

'Were you seen?' Splinter asked. Leo shook his head. He knew, and so did his brothers, that they would always have to keep their existence a secret. They were trained to help people in trouble, but even people in trouble would have a hard time understanding mutant ninja turtles, to say nothing of teenage. Secrecy was one of their most powerful weapons.

'You must always strike hard and fade away without a trace,' Splinter reminded the Turtles.

Don flashed a look at Raph. He'd come pretty close to breaking that rule when he'd tried to grab his sai from the lady in the car-park. It didn't take a dirty look from Don to upset Raph. He was already angry and disappointed in himself.

'I lost a sai!' he burst out.

'Then it is gone,' Splinter said calmly.

'But I can get it *back*, I can—'

'Raphael, let it go,' Splinter counselled. Raph stopped talking, holding in his thoughts and his worries.

Mike, in the meantime, was having a hard time holding in his appetite. He was already on the phone. 'OK, the one with the pepperoni, mushrooms, onion, sausage, green pepper. No anchovies. Not one, you understand? And we want the crust thick and chewy, not soggy . . . ' He continued with his very specific cooking instructions while Splinter addressed all four of the Turtles.

'Your ninja skills are reaching their peak,' he said. 'Only one truly important lesson remains, but must wait. I know it is hard for you here, underground. Your teenage minds are broad, eager, but you must never stop practising the art of ninja – the art of invisibility, and – *Michaelangelo*!'

Mike had just got to the part about extra cheese when Splinter called his name, reminding Mike that his first job was to listen to Splinter. Pizza could come later. But, Mike hoped, not *too* much later. He got off the phone and listened to Splinter.

'You are still young, but one day I will be gone. Use my teachings wisely.'

Splinter, *gone*? The Turtles could barely think of the idea. Sure, he was old, but—

'I suggest we all meditate now on the events of this evening.'

The old rat closed his eyes.

Splinter was terrific, there was no doubt about it and the Turtles agreed on it, but sometimes the ninja stuff went just a little bit too far for their teenage hearts. This was a time for celebration, not meditation.

Don slipped the tape into the player and Mike pushed the button. It was time to rock and roll!

'Do-doop dooby dooby *wa* wah!' Mike and Don began to dance to the music. Leo looked on nervously. He didn't think Splinter would like it. He was right.

Splinter was glaring at Mike and Don. 'Well, uh, it's sort of like meditating, you know?' Splinter didn't seem to agree. Mike and Don turned off the music and sat down for meditation.

Raph, still upset about the loss of his sai, wasn't in a meditating or celebrating mood – at least not with his friends. He slipped into his upper-world disguise, a trench coat and a felt hat. He told his friends he was going to the cinema. Before anybody could object, he was out the door.

Raph was like that sometimes. The others just left him to his own ways. Besides, the pizza would be there soon. Mike looked at his watch. *Twenty-three minutes*, he said to himself. *If the delivery man isn't late again.*

3

In another part of town, Casey Jones sat and watched his television set. He didn't like what he saw. A crime reporter named June was telling the public about more and more violent crimes. He tried another channel. A woman was about to be eaten by a gigantic monster from Japan. A third channel showed three men shooting their guns to the tune of a dozen police sirens. On another channel, cowboys and Indians were fighting one another. Casey turned back to the news. It was less violent.

'There is no end in sight to the crime wave, and a police spokesman today could offer no further information on progress. There isn't any,' she said.

Disgusted, Casey turned off the television set. He looked around his apartment. The walls were covered with sports and martial arts posters. Almost every surface was cluttered with sports equipment. Casey liked sports, combat with rules, tests of skill where everybody had a chance. He didn't much like violence and he especially didn't like crime waves. The trouble was, what could he do about it? He looked at his hockey mask. He looked at his golf bag full of bats, sticks, and golf clubs. He got an idea.

Down in the sewer outside the Turtles' den, Donatello rolled out some lazy S-curves on his skateboard. Michaelangelo sat near by hunched under the manhole to the street that they thought of as their front door. Meditation was over, it was pizza time. Almost. If only the pizza would get there.

'Nice night,' Donatello remarked, looking up at the stars through the grating.

Michaelangelo wasn't in the mood for a discussion of the weather. 'Pizza dude's got thirty seconds,' he grumbled.

Donatello sat down next to his brother. 'Hey, Mikie, you ever think about what Splinter said tonight – like, I mean, what it would be like, uh, without him?'

Michaelangelo didn't answer for a minute. He didn't like to think about serious things. It seemed to him that there were too many serious things in life. He'd rather think about pizza.

'Time's up! Three bucks off!' he announced.

Donatello understood that some things were just hard for Mike. It didn't mean he didn't care; it didn't mean he didn't think. Mike just didn't like to talk about it.

Just then there was a shuffling sound above, and the grumbling of an unhappy person who couldn't find his way.

'Swell! Where the heck is this dumb pizza supposed to be delivered?'

'You're standing on it, dude!' Mike announced.

The delivery man jumped three feet in the air with fright. 'What the . . . !?!?'

Michaelangelo stuck a note up through the grate. 'Just slip the pizza down here, man,' he said.

The pizza came down. Then the man yelled at Michaelangelo. 'Hey, you're three bucks short, man!'

'And you're two minutes late, dude!' Mike said. Then he began talking like a Chinese philosopher. 'Wise man say: Forgiveness is divine, but never pay full price for a late pizza!'

Mike and Don hurried towards the den's door with their pizza. Above them on the street, the pizza man stared at the grate where he'd delivered a pizza, and been taken for three dollars. He shook his head.

'I got to get a new route,' he said.

Down in the den, Mike borrowed one of Leo's katana and used it for what he thought it did best. He tossed the fully cooked pizza into the air. Before it landed, Mike swished at it four times, cutting it into eight exactly equal pieces.

'It slices, it dices, and *yes*, it makes french fries *three* different ways!' he joked, sounding like an ad for the dice-o-matic that he'd seen one night when he'd stayed up too late watching TV.

Eight perfectly cut slices of pizza landed right where the Turtles could eat them. Not a minute too soon!

4

Raphael made a face as he left the cinema. He'd seen *E.T. – The Extra Terrestrial*. He didn't like it at all.

'Yuk,' he said to himself. 'Where do they come *up* with this stuff?' After all, how could any self-respecting Teenage Mutant Ninja Turtle enjoy a far-fetched story like *E.T.*?

He pulled up the collar on his trench coat and began the walk home. It wasn't long, however, before he got sidetracked. Right near by, two hoodlums grabbed a little old lady's purse and began running away with it – towards Raph!

It was easy work. Raphael stuck out his foot, tripped the one carrying the purse, and caught the booty as it flew out of the hoodlum's hand. He tossed the purse to the astonished lady. The hoodlums were too surprised to react. They just ran away to the relative safety of Central Park at night.

Raph watched them go and followed them into the park just to be sure they wouldn't cause any more trouble. It turned out it wasn't the hoodlums who

caused the next piece of trouble. While they were trying to escape into darkness, Raphael saw a guy in a hockey mask, carrying a golf bag filled with bats, clubs, and sticks, attack the fleeing hoodlums.

'*That* was a crime, you purse-grabbing pukes – and *this* is the penalty!' the masked man said before he began beating up the hoodlums with all the tools from his bag of tricks. 'Two minutes for slashing. Two minutes for hooking. And, my personal favourite: two minutes for high sticking!' The hoodlums were at his mercy!

Raph thought it was one thing to frighten off a pair of purse-snatchers and another altogether to beat them to a pulp with a hockey stick. He actually felt sorry for them. Something had to be done! Raph stepped in.

'How about five minutes for roughing, pal?' Raph asked the masked man.

The man looked at him, surprised. 'Who made you the referee? You did your part. Now these guys need a lesson!'

'Not like that, they don't,' Raph said. 'And not from you.'

The hoodlums took advantage of the pause in the action. They ran away. Neither Raph nor the masked man noticed them leave. Each was too upset by the other's anger to care about the hoodlums.

'Looks like *you're* the one who needs the lesson,' the masked man said. He took out a baseball bat and began swinging. It didn't take long before the tables turned and Raphael overpowered the masked man. When he'd been beaten, he challenged Raphael one more time – with something to think about.

'Man, you're crazy!' the masked man said.

'*I'm* crazy?'

'Yeah, and dangerous!' the man told Raphael.

Raphael thought that was odd. That was just what he thought about the masked man. He watched as the masked man disappeared into the darkness of the park. Then it was time to return home.

'Raphael, come sit by me,' Splinter said, surprising Raph on his return.

Raphael didn't want to talk to Splinter then. Raph was uncomfortable with what the masked man had said to him and he didn't want to think about it. Splinter had a way of making the Turtles think about things they didn't want to think about.

'Could this wait until morning?' Raph asked.

'You will listen now,' Splinter said. Raph sat down. Splinter lit a candle and began speaking.

'My master Yoshi's first rule was, *Possess the right thinking. Only then can one receive the gifts of strength, knowledge, and peace.* I have tried to ease the anger you have, Raphael, but there is so much! Anger clouds the mind. Turned inwards, it is an enemy. You do not have to face this enemy alone. Do not forget your brothers, and do not forget me.'

Raphael thought about his anger. In a way, his anger was just as violent a weapon as the masked man's hockey sticks and baseball bats. If that was true, then what he had done to the masked man was no better than dropping out of a tree to attack two hoodlums who had already learned their lesson.

5

April O'Neil was looking forward to getting to work that day. She was pretty sure she was near a breakthrough on the crime wave – if only she could pin down Chief Sterns.

First, however, she had to cope with her boss. Charles Pennington had shown up at her apartment while she was getting ready for work. He had a lot on his mind, too, and none of it was helping April. He was just getting in her way while she combed her hair. Charles had even brought his teenage son, Danny, who was sitting quietly in her living room. Danny was a troubled boy. April thought Charles had brought him so he could keep an eye on him.

'You could have called me last night, you know?' Charles began. 'Call it a quirk, but I like to *know* when one of my best reporters has been mugged.'

April combed her hair as she answered. 'I wasn't mugged, Charles.' Strictly speaking, she hadn't been mugged. She'd just been attacked by four thugs who were in the middle of a robbery. And then she'd been rescued by – whom? She remembered the funny three-pronged dagger in her bag. There was more to this story than *anybody* knew.

Charles seemed genuinely concerned. 'From now on, Security's escorting you out to that beat-up van of yours at night.'

'Yes, sir,' April said, saluting. Some things weren't worth arguing about. They went into April's living room.

Charles sighed. 'What's going on out there?' he asked, looking out the window. 'There's so much crime!'

Now *this* was something April wanted to talk about with Charles. 'I'll tell you this,' she began. 'I've talked to a lot of people in the Japanese community here and I'm awfully suspicious about the crime wave. Sterns is going to have some answering to do at the press conference this afternoon!'

April realized that might not make Charles happy. He was friends with the mayor and every time she gave Sterns a hard time, the mayor called Charles. She decided to change the subject. 'Say, how's school going, Danny?' she asked the sullen teenager. Danny began to answer, but Charles answered for him.

'Oh, wonderful,' Charles said sarcastically. 'So wonderful, in fact, that I have to drive him there every morning now just to make sure he goes!'

Danny pulled his headphones over his ears. 'That's what he does when he wants to ignore me,' Charles said. 'I don't even know where he got the earphones!'

April knew from the look on his face that of all the things that worried Charles, Danny was the most worrisome, and the one he felt most helpless about. She felt sorry for Charles. She also felt sorry for Danny.

However, two hours later, when April had to pay a taxi fare and found her wallet was empty, she wasn't so sure she felt sorry for Danny. Although, like Charles, she didn't know *where* Danny had got the earphones, she suspected she knew *how* he had got them.

6

That afternoon, Donatello flipped on the TV to watch *Wheel of Fortune*, but it wasn't on. Instead, there was a news conference going on. Police Chief Sterns was talking about the crime wave. The other Turtles joined him. They were interested in this news.

'We are presently executing a plan of redeployment that will minimize response time by maximizing coordination between patrol units in a decentralized networking scheme.'

Nobody understood what the chief had just said. The Turtles didn't think even Chief Sterns had understood the gobbledygook!

'Would you mind repeating that, Chief?' a reporter asked. 'In English?'

The camera pulled back to show the reporter. It was the same woman the Turtles had saved in the Channel Three car-park. It was April O'Neil!

'Hey! That's her!' Donatello said.

Michaelangelo couldn't believe how pretty April was. 'I'm in love,' he told his friends.

'Shhh,' Leo said. 'Let's listen.'

'Chief Sterns, what do you know about The Foot Clan?' she asked.

The chief squirmed. He didn't seem to like the question. 'There is no evidence—'

'Then you deny that there is such a thing as The Foot?'

'I'm not denying anything,' Chief Sterns blustered.

April had learned a lot about The Foot from some Japanese friends. It was an ancient ninja clan sworn to destroy orderly society with criminal acts. Its goal was total power. The city's current crime wave certainly looked like something a clan like that would be involved in. Chief Sterns didn't believe it at all.

'If you'll excuse me, I have more important matters to deal with.'

As he walked away, April turned to the camera. 'We can only hope that one of them has to do with solving these crimes!'

'She's great!' Michaelangelo said. His friends agreed.

'And she's got my sai,' Raphael said. Before anybody could stop him, he grabbed his upper-world disguise and headed for the door. He knew just where he could find April.

The Turtles were not the only ones watching April's interview and Raphael was not the only one who wanted to find her. In another part of town a man called Shredder watched April's interview. When she asked about The Foot, the man sat up, startled, angry. The Foot was a deep secret. He didn't want anybody to know about their mission, especially a nosy reporter.

He lofted a ninja dagger at the screen. It hit April right between the eyes.

Then he turned to his second-in-command, Tatsu, and nodded. The man knew what must be done.

April entered the subway station near City Hall, just missing a train. She was alone on the platform – for a few seconds.

'We've been looking for you, Ms O'Neil,' someone said. She turned and saw four men, dressed in black ninja outfits with hoods.

'What, am I behind on my television payments again?' she joked weakly.

The men didn't laugh. Instead, they told her to stop talking about things she didn't know anything about. Or *else*.

April didn't like the situation at all. The Foot began slapping her and it hurt. She could be in real trouble. Then she remembered the odd dagger that had saved her in the car-park. It was in her bag. She reached for it, but before she could strike, The Foot knocked it out of her hand. It skittered along the subway platform. She was defenceless!

April swung her bag at her attackers. She managed to knock one of them down, but three more attacked. The last thing she saw before she lost consciousness was a green three-fingered hand picking up the sai.

Once Raphael had his sai back, he was at full strength. He didn't know who was attacking April or why, but he knew it was his job to save her. He fought like a cyclone, beating off April's attackers just long enough to reach April.

She was unconscious, but breathing. He had to get her – and himself – out of there. He liked to fight to win, but sometimes it was wiser to fight to escape.

A train was coming into the station. Raphael had an idea. While continuing to fight with one hand, he picked April up with the other. Just a split second before the train arrived, he dashed in front of it, going to the safety of the far side of the tracks. While the train blocked April's attackers from following him, he made the getaway, carrying April.

The subways in New York were just one part of the vast underworld of the city. The sewers were another. Raphael wasn't worried about finding his way home from there. He wasn't even worried about giving away the Turtles' secret. The only thing he was worried about was saving April O'Neil's life.

In fact, he was so worried about that that he never heard the footsteps that trailed him through the tunnels.

7

'**A**re you crazy?' Leonardo asked Raph as he put April's limp body on the sofa in the Turtles' den.

A lot of people seemed to be asking Raphael that these days. For once, he was certain that he was not.

'Why?' Leonardo asked.

'*Why?* Oh, I don't know. I thought we should redecorate – you know, a couple of throw cushions, a TV news reporter . . . What do you think? Anyway, she got jumped in the subway. I had to bring her here.'

Splinter entered the room. All arguing stopped. Splinter took one look at April's wounds and began issuing orders. 'Herb jar. Cold washcloth. Pillow.'

The Turtles scurried into action. Splinter sat next to her to take care of her.

April's eyes fluttered open. There, in front of her, was a four-foot-tall rat and four giant turtles standing on their hind legs and wearing strange outfits. She did the most logical thing she could think of. She screamed.

'Ahhhhhhh!'

'Hi,' Michaelangelo said. He was always friendly.

'Ahhhhhhhhh!' She gasped for breath and then began babbling. She thought she was dead.

She tried to stand up and run away. Splinter tried to calm her. She couldn't believe she was hearing a rat – a *giant* rat – talk.

'It's really quite simple, Ms O'Neil,' Splinter began.

April was too weak and too confused to protest. She sat back down and listened to Splinter's story.

Once Splinter had been a normal rat living in Japan, where he was the pet of a ninja master named Yoshi. He had learned all about ninja by mimicking Yoshi's movements. When Yoshi had had to leave Japan, they'd come to America and eventually Splinter had had to fend for himself.

'One day I saw an old blind man crossing the street, unaware of the truck barrelling down upon him. The truck swerved to avoid him. The truck was loaded with metal canisters of weird chemicals. One of them bounced off the truck. There was a little boy on the pavement, holding a glass jar. In the jar were four baby turtles—'

'That was us!' Michaelangelo interrupted.

'Shhhh!' his brothers said. This was their favourite story. It told where they'd come from.

Splinter continued. 'The canister smashed into the jar and then crashed on to the street. Both the jar and the canister broke. Soon the little turtles were covered with a glowing ooze flowing out of the canister. The little boy's mother wouldn't let him touch them. When they'd gone, I put the little turtles in an old coffee jar and brought them to my home here in the sewer. When I woke up the next morning, the jar was tipped over – for the turtles had doubled in size! I, too, was growing.

My body grew, but my brain grew even more. I got smarter and smarter as they got bigger and bigger.

'Soon they began to stand upright, copying my every movement. I was amazed at how intelligent they seemed, but I was even more amazed when they began speaking! They were almost as smart as I was. I could teach them everything I had learned from my master Yoshi. And when it came time to name them, I took a copy of a Renaissance art book that I had found in a storm drain. Now, I would like you to meet Leonardo, Michaelangelo, Donatello, and Raphael.'

Each turtle bowed as Splinter introduced him.

'Get real!' April said.

8

It took the Turtles and Splinter another few minutes to convince April she wasn't dreaming, but she finally came round. She even agreed to let them take her home.

When they got to her apartment, April told them the only thing she had to eat in her house was left-over pizza.

'Let's *go* for it!' Michaelangelo said. That surprised April. She thought turtles just ate lettuce!

'So, what do you guys, uh, like on your pizza?' she asked.

'Just the regular stuff,' Michaelangelo told her. 'You know, flies, stinkbugs, slugs—'

April gasped. Mike realized she wasn't into Turtle humour, yet.

'It was a *joke*,' he told her. April laughed, a little.

The pizza was great and the Turtles found they could have a lot of fun with April. She learned that it was fun to be with the Turtles.

Mike did his Rocky impression. April laughed very hard. She never would have thought of Rocky as green!

'Wait, wait, I've got another one.'

'Oh, no – not James Cagney!' Raph groaned.

Michaelangelo crouched into a boxer's stance and began jabbing at the air with his fists. 'You dirty rat!' he said. 'You killed my brother. You dirty rat!'

It was a good impression! 'Hey, that must be Splinter's favourite!' she said.

The Turtles looked at her for a second. They were surprised.

'It was a *joke*,' she said, imitating Michaelangelo. All of them laughed. The Turtles realized then that April was their friend and as long as she could laugh with them, she'd be a good friend, too.

It was time to go. 'We'd better get back to Splinter,' Leo said. 'He worries.' Sometimes it was hard to stop having fun just because Splinter might worry about them. Most of the time, though, it was comforting to know that he cared enough to worry.

'Will I ever see you guys again?' April asked.

'That depends on how fast you restock your pizza,' Leo told her.

'Deal!' April said.

The Turtles left April's apartment building, climbed down the nearest storm drain, and made their way back to their den.

As soon as they got near the door, though, they all knew something was wrong. The door was open, flapping loosely, and when they went in, the place was a total shambles. The worst part, though, was that there was no sign of Splinter.

He'd been ratnapped!

They realized that the thugs who'd attacked April in the subway must have followed Raphael through the sewers to their den. But who would want to capture Splinter? Who would do something *that* evil? Maybe it was the kind of person who would mastermind a crime wave!

The Turtles needed help. They needed a friend. They needed April.

At the same time that the Turtles found their troubles were beginning, Chief Sterns thought it was possible that *his* troubles were coming to an end. He had just the thing he needed to get Charles Pennington to keep that pesky reporter, April O'Neil, off his back.

He held in his hand an arrest file for Daniel B. Pennington. The teenager had been picked up for shoplifting in an electronics shop.

Chief Sterns reached for his phone and dialed a number. A man answered. 'Charles Pennington?' he asked. He smiled to himself.

9

Bright and early the next morning there was a knock at April's door, startling her, and four Turtles, awake. They'd had a long night, talking about Splinter, talking about what they could do and what they couldn't. They'd all stayed at April's. Nobody knew she'd have company so early in the morning!

'Who is it?' April asked.

'It's me, Charles,' Pennington said from outside.

'It's my boss!' April whispered to the Turtles. 'Can you guys, uh—' She looked around. There wasn't a Turtle in sight. '—hide?'

She put on her dressing-gown and opened the door for Charles. He barged into her apartment. Danny trailed behind him. The boy had a sullen, angry look.

While his father talked to April, Danny sat down and picked up a copy of *Sports Illustrated* to read. Next to him was a floor lamp. It was the ugliest lamp he'd ever seen. It looked as if it had been made out of a giant turtle. Not only was it ugly, but it wouldn't turn on, either. He moved to her sofa, where there was a light on already. He put his feet up on April's coffee table. That looked like a turtle, too. It was as ugly as the lamp. What's with these turtles? Danny wondered. He forgot about it, though, as soon as he saw that there was an article about college basketball in the magazine. He didn't pay any more attention to his father and April, either.

'April, listen, I've, uh . . . ' Charles stuttered. April thought he seemed very uncomfortable, and when she heard what he had to say, she knew why. 'I've been thinking about this crime story. You've been working on it too hard lately. I think you should take some time off and let someone else handle it, you know?'

Suddenly, April was very awake, and very angry. 'Charles! What are you talking about? This is *my* story. No way! And besides, I'm certain, if I can just push Sterns a little harder—' She began washing her face.

Charles looked panicked. 'Oh, no, April. Not that! Don't push Sterns any more, OK? At least not today?'

April couldn't believe her ears. 'Charles, what's with you today?'

'Oh, nothing. I just thought you'd like some time off, that's all.'

'Well, I wouldn't,' April said. 'Hand me a towel, will you?'

Charles looked around for one. There wasn't one in sight. 'Where do you—' he began, searching. He reached for the shower curtain. April couldn't let him open it, though. She was certain Mike was hiding in the bath. She couldn't let him see the Turtles!

'Charles, no!' she shrieked, but it was too late. The curtain flew open and . . . ! Nothing. There was just an empty bath. April thought there was a lot to be said for the art of ninja-invisibility!

'What's wrong?' Charles asked.

Now April had to explain her shriek. 'Wrong? Well, now you've gone and seen my unsightly bath ring!' She snapped the shower curtain closed and turned to Charles. 'Out!' she said. 'Out! Out! Out!' After all, what business did he have in her bathroom anyway? 'I have to get ready for work. There's a crime wave going on and I'm a crime reporter!'

'Sure you won't reconsider?'

April spoke to Danny for the first time. 'Hey, Danny, tell your dad to relax,' she joked.

'I *wish*,' Danny said. April didn't think he was joking at all.

It took a few more minutes to get Charles out of her place, but she finally succeeded. Turtles began appearing from every corner of the apartment.

'That was close!' Mike said, suddenly standing behind April. She was so surprised that she jumped about three feet. 'Time to switch to decaf, April,' he teased. She smiled, a little.

Charles grumbled as he sat behind the wheel of his car. Nothing was going right for him. Sterns was on his back. Danny was in trouble with the law, and sure as anything, April was going to try to corner Sterns, which would make Sterns corner Charles – or worse, Danny. Charles took it out on Danny.

'I just don't get it, Danny. I make enough money to provide for more than the both of us, and you're out stealing. Why?'

'I don't know,' Danny answered.

'You don't know. What were you going to do with that car stereo anyway, or don't you know *that* either?'

'Sorry,' Danny said.

Charles couldn't help himself. It was too much. He exploded at his son. 'Not as sorry as you're going to be after school!' he began as he pulled his car to a stop at a light. 'When I get home—'

Without a word Danny opened the door of the car and bolted. He disappeared into an alley before Charles could even open his door.

If things had looked bad before . . .

10

It was almost time for Assembly in Shredder's warehouse. Shredder was the ninja master of The Foot Clan in New York City. His headquarters were in an abandoned warehouse in Brooklyn. Shredder's second-in-command, Tatsu, hurried to the assembly area. Tatsu was a big man, bald-headed and fierce. He wore a black dogi with a small dragon emblem on it. It was the sign of The Foot.

First he had to pass through the Beginners' section. Shredder's new recruits were having the time of their lives. They were playing video games and pool, smoking cigarettes, and using bad language. They were doing everything their parents had ever told them not to do. Tatsu knew that when they had had enough fun, they would move on.

He strode into the first-level training area. There were no pool tables and video games here. It was more like a ninja playground. Each of the boys wore a uniform belt and a headband with The Foot's dragon emblem on it while they worked in the training area. There the

recruits were studying the fine art of pocket-picking.

Four boys surrounded a dummy wearing an overcoat covered with little bells. In most pick-pocket training exercises, the purpose was to remove the dummy's wallet without ringing a bell. That was too easy for The Foot.

On a signal from the trainer, the boys attacked the dummy. In a matter of seconds, every bell had been removed from the dummy's coat. Not a sound had been made. Tatsu grunted. He was satisfied.

In the next room, more serious work was taking place. This was where trainees, now wearing dogis like Tatsu's, studied the deadly art of karate. There were no rules here, except one: Win. Losers were carried away.

One combatant had just finished off an opponent when Tatsu entered. The teenager was pleased with his work. Tatsu thought he had more to learn. Tatsu stepped into the arena and took up where the loser had left off. Without warning, he attacked the tall teenager. The tall teenager blocked every punch and kick with incredible speed, almost as if he could anticipate Tatsu's next move. Tatsu was pleased. He stopped his attack, stepped back, and bowed, keeping his eyes glued to the teenager.

The teenager returned the bow, looking politely down to the floor. Tatsu attacked. In a split second he had the boy pinned.

'*Never* lower your eyes to an enemy!' he hissed.

It was a lesson the boy would remember for a long time.

Tatsu left the room, heading for the assembly area. The bell would ring soon; the boys would gather soon. He would be there, ready.

On his way to the assembly area, he passed a dark corner of the warehouse. Tatsu knew what was there. He didn't need to look. For in a corner, hanging by his shackled wrists, was Splinter, prisoner of The Foot Clan.

11

When the gong began ringing, Danny Pennington put down his pool cue. He hadn't been in the warehouse gang long, but he knew when to stop playing. He followed his newfound friends into the assembly area.

It was Danny's first look at the entire clan. He was proud to be part of it, and when he saw the advanced students, he became excited. They looked so cool in their black dogis. Being cool and being tough was a sure way to avoid any stupid lectures from his father. He'd be that cool. He'd be that tough!

When all the members of The Foot were assembled, Shredder arrived. Danny couldn't believe it. The man was something else. He was the baddest, meanest man Danny had *ever* seen. He marched on to centre stage, wearing a flowing black cape and a metal ninja helmet that covered all of his face, except for an eye slit that he could see through.

Tatsu stepped behind Shredder and removed the cloak, very carefully. Then Danny knew how Shredder got his name. He was wearing a dogi, but it was totally covered with razor-sharp ninja armour. Danny gasped.

Then four boys, the thugs who had attacked April in the car-park and lost a battle to the Turtles, were brought out and stood facing Shredder. While the boys watched, Tatsu placed an ornate red headband on Shredder's shoulder. Danny realized that Shredder was going to fight all four boys at once, and if one of them could grab the headband, he'd be spared. Danny didn't know what these boys had done to deserve this punishment, but he vowed that, whatever it was, he'd never do it!

Shredder attacked. Danny had never seen anything like it. His movements were so sure, so clean, so fast, that it almost seemed to be in slow motion. The thugs didn't have a chance against the master. Not one of them ever got close to the prized headband. All of them got hurt, but not one got seriously hurt. It was as if Shredder were playing with them. He'd slash one across the arm, then another on the cheek. If he wanted to kill them, he could do it, easily. But he didn't. Danny wondered why.

The thugs were helped out of the arena. Carefully, Tatsu removed the headband, which hadn't moved.

Shredder turned to all of his students and spoke for the first time.

'Money paid as bail for your freedom is money lost to us. These four have now paid their debt. Their punishment was just, as it always is in our family. They will wear their scars proudly as reminders of their quest to become *full* members of The Foot.'

At that instant a teenager in a black dogi came and knelt in front of Shredder. Shredder put a ninja hood on his head. Danny knew that that boy was now a full member of The Foot. Danny also knew that that was what he wanted to be more than anything. He'd work, he'd study, he'd learn. For once in his life, he'd do something right.

'Our family grows.' Shredder began speaking again. 'And soon the city itself will be our playground, to use as we please – rewarding ourselves and our friends, punishing our enemies.' He paused and then looked up at the teenagers. 'There is a new enemy,' he said. 'Freaks of nature who interfere with our business. You are my eyes and ears. Find them. Together we will punish these creatures – these turtles!'

Turtles? Danny thought. Why did that ring a bell? Then he remembered the turtle lamp and table in April's apartment – ugly stuff. So why hadn't those ugly things been there the *first* time Danny was at April's? Suddenly Danny had the feeling that there could be a shortcut to his own dogi and ninja hood. Suddenly he had more courage than he ever would have thought possible.

Danny Pennington raised his hand.

12

In April's apartment the next day, the Turtles were lazing around, watching television. For once, though, they weren't watching quiz shows, *Gilligan's Island* repeats, or soap operas. They were watching April being interviewed. She was telling all about being attacked by the ninja in the subway station. The Turtles thought she was very smart.

'I'm convinced that these men were affiliated with a secret organisation known as The Foot.'

'The Foot?' June, another reporter, asked, confused.

April smiled. 'Yeah, I know. It sounds like a funky club for podiatrists, but I've spoken with a lot of Japanese-Americans recently and they tell me this crime wave reminds them of a secret band of ninja thieves called The Foot. The evidence is convincing, but so far the police are treating this like a joke!'

Charles Pennington shuddered when he heard April say those words. It was just the kind of thing that would make Chief Sterns angry. And if Chief Sterns got angry, Danny Pennington would have to pay the price.

'Mr Pennington?' his secretary said, opening the door of his office softly. 'Telephone call. It's City Hall.'

Charles groaned and reached for the phone.

'She's such a good reporter!' Leonardo said.

'She's smart,' said Donatello.

'Shhhhhh!' said Michaelangelo. 'I think the best part is still to come.'

The screen flickered as the camera got a close-up shot of April's lovely face. 'There's another mystery, April,' June said. 'How did you manage to get away from those subway attackers?'

'Incredible as it may seem, a citizen of this city actually came to my rescue. So I'd like to take this opportunity to express my gratitude.' April looked right into the camera. 'Thanks, Raphael!' she said, winking.

'Woooooooo!' Leonardo, Michaelangelo, and Donatello all teased in a single voice. Raphael shrank into his shell.

'Hey, look! I think he's blushing!' Donatello said.

'I am not!' Raphael said, but he was sure he was turning red. Raphael didn't like to be teased and sometimes it made him very angry. He loved his brothers, but he hated feeling this way, especially when there were more important things to think about.

'So what do we do now?' he asked, trying to change the subject.

'What do you mean, "what do we do now?"' Leo asked.

'*Splinter's* out there!' Raph said, reminding his brothers of the serious situation.

It didn't work, though. All the others wanted to do was eat. Raphael was too angry to eat.

'What *can* we do about it? April's our only link to these guys! We have to wait until she comes up with something!'

Raphael was steamed. 'Oh, so that's the plan from our great leader, huh? Just sit here on our tails?'

Leonardo turned on him. 'I never said I was your great leader!'

'Well, you sure act like it sometimes!'

'Yeah, well, you act like a jerk sometimes, you know that? And, this attitude of yours isn't helping anything!'

That was as much as Raphael could take. He spun on his heels and stormed out the door. He just had to be by himself. He headed for the stairs and went up. The street was no place to be alone. Raphael needed a rooftop.

It was a warm summer afternoon. A few blocks from April's apartment, Casey Jones was relaxing on his own rooftop, stretched out on a beach chair. He wasn't wearing his hockey mask, though it was handy – just in case. He took a sip of his soda and enjoyed the afternoon breeze. He sat up and looked at the city below him.

It was so hot that everything seemed to be still. Everything, that is, except a small green dot moving on a rooftop several blocks away. There was something familiar about that green dot. Casey grabbed his binoculars and focused them. It sure was familiar. It was the green guy who had attacked him in the park.

Then Casey looked again. The green guy didn't know it, but he'd been spotted by someone else. The fire escape that led to the rooftop where the green guy sat was positively swarming with black-clad ninja types.

The green guy was about to get into a lot of trouble.

Casey believed in fairness. No matter how tough the green guy was, this wasn't going to be a fair fight. It was time to go to work. Casey reached for his mask.

13

Michaelangelo, Donatello, and Leonardo finished their snack and returned to the television in April's apartment. *The Flintstones* was on. It was one of their favourites.

'Man, that Dino could *act*!' Mike said. 'You know, they should make this show into a film!'

'Right,' Don said sarcastically. 'How're they going to make a cartoon into a movie?'

Before Mike could answer, the door opened and April came in. The Turtles told her how great she'd been in the interview. She said she hoped it would get results. Then she offered to give the Turtles the grand tour of her father's antique shop in the basement of her building.

'It's really more like a junk shop,' she said. 'I only run it part-time now, and it doesn't make any money. I do it mostly because of my dad. He loved junk! Ready?'

The Turtles nodded.

Then April noticed somebody was missing. 'Hey, where's Raphael?' she asked.

'He's by himself,' Michaelangelo said. 'He just needs to blow off some steam.'

'Ooo-oomph!' Raph said as three Foot Clan ninja slammed his body against a wall. His sai clattered over the edge of the roof. Raph got his breath. 'I thought you guys used the subway,' he joked, recalling his last battle with the dogi-clad thugs when he saved April. The Foot attacked him. He repelled their attack, sending several of them down the fire escape. More took their place. He knocked them unconscious. 'You guys must be studying the abridged book of ninja fighting!' he joked, facing his last two attackers.

That was his last joke. For those two were followed by dozens more. Soon the whole roof was swarming with Foot, and they all had the same goal: Raphael.

'Hasn't Raphael been gone a long time?' April asked the others as they explored the junk shop.

'Nah. He does this all the time. He *likes* it,' Donatello told her.

The Foot dragged Raphael's beaten body down the fire escape. His shell thumped along the metal steps. He was completely unconscious.

'Are you *sure* Raphael's OK?' April asked, leading the trio back up to her apartment.

'Don't worry,' Donatello assured her. 'He'll probably be back any minute now, threatening to huff and puff and blow your house—'

He was interrupted by the tremendous crash of breaking glass as Raphael's body came flying through

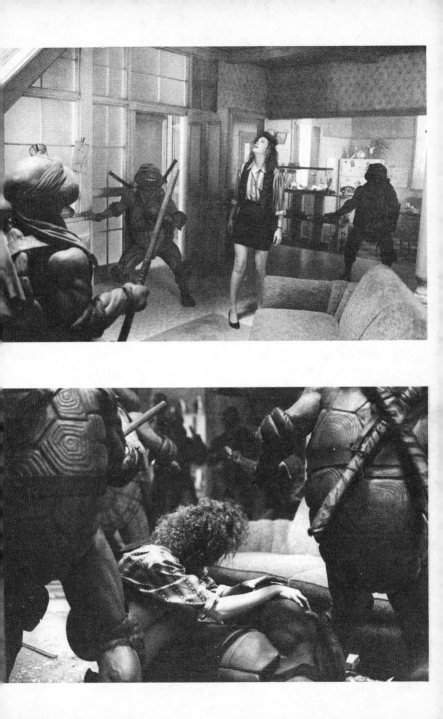

April's window. Before his brothers could begin to take care of him, the entire apartment was completely filled with The Foot. Leonardo, Michaelangelo, and Donatello were fighting for their own lives as well as Raphael's and April's.

The Turtles were good. They were very good. Splinter had taught them well. They had learned to fight honourably and well. They'd learned to win, but they had never learned to beat enemies who outnumbered them by one hundred to one. They didn't have a chance to win. And then the odds got worse. More Foot arrived. There were so many ninja soldiers and the fighting was so fierce that the old structure of April's apartment couldn't take it any more. The floor collapsed. Dozens of Foot, plus April and the Turtles, tumbled helplessly into the junk shop. Fighting resumed.

'Hey, one of these guys must know where Splinter is!' Leonardo shouted to Don and Mike. 'Don't knock them all out!'

Mike watched a new wave of Foot arrive. 'I don't think that'll be a problem, Leo!' he said. They all knew he was right.

'Man, we could really use Raph about now!' Michaelangeo said, trying to hold off a half-dozen attackers by himself. Raph was out of the battle, though. April was with him. He was alive, but he was unconscious.

Then more reinforcements arrived – this time on the side of the Turtles. Casey Jones entered the shop in full battle gear – hockey mask and goalie's stick!

'Who is *that*?' Leo asked.

Michaelangelo looked at Casey Jones. He was enormous and he was going to help *them*. 'Wayne Gretzky? On steroids?' he suggested. Right then it didn't matter who he was. The only thing that mattered was that he was on their side.

'Eeeeee-hah!' Casey said, jumping into the fray. 'Hockey Night in Canada!' He began swinging his stick. Foot began falling. But not enough of them. There were too many to be beaten.

The only chance they had was to escape.

'Follow me,' April said, pulling Raphael into a corner of the shop. With Leo's help, they moved a bookcase aside.

'My grandfather used this secret entrance when he was selling something more than junk during Prohibition,' April explained. 'It might just slow these guys down enough for us to get out of here!'

As soon as the door swung open, the Turtles and April were in the tunnel. Casey, who was not as exhausted as the Turtles, held off The Foot for the others to escape first. When they were safe, he prepared to enter the tunnel himself.

Just before the door closed, Casey heard April's phone ring. He heard her machine answer it. He heard the message. It was Charles Pennington.

'Look, I'm sorry, April, but you're fired . . . '

It was a perfect end to a perfect day.

14

Casey drove April's van for their escape. The Turtles tended to Raphael and to their own wounds. April looked out the rear window of the van. She watched the fire that was engulfing her shop and her apartment. It seemed as if everything that mattered to her was going up in smoke. It was one thing when thieves stole money and jewellery. That was bad enough. It hurt more, however, when they stole your past.

The last thing April saw before Casey turned on to the highway was a boy with a Foot headband, staring at the van. He looked familiar to April. Danny Pennington? *No way*, April told herself. Then she remembered the missing money from her wallet. Maybe, she thought.

The old van continued to bounce its way towards freedom and safety.

Meanwhile, Splinter was still a prisoner in Shredder's warehouse. He had been beaten by Shredder and had new wounds to prove it. It didn't matter. In spite of the pain, he was feeling good. Shredder was angry because the Turtles had fought so hard and had hurt so many of his men. If Shredder was that angry, it meant the Turtles had escaped and were still alive!

Splinter looked up when a boy walked in. It was Danny Pennington. He seemed almost lost in thought.

'How can a face so young wear so many burdens?' Splinter asked.

'You can *talk*?' Danny asked in surprise.

'Yes,' Splinter said. 'And I can also listen.'

Danny didn't want to talk then. He just needed to think. Things were so complicated!

Danny left Splinter and wandered into the Foot locker room. There he saw the battered warriors resting and hanging out after the battle. Danny stood to the side and observed. He'd seen these boys fight bravely, nearly losing to the Turtles. They were so skilled, so strong – yet . . .

Suddenly the door flew open and Tatsu marched in. He was furious at the warriors because the Turtles had survived and escaped. He was angry at everybody, but he began picking on one warrior particularly. He kicked the boy and then punched him fiercely. The boy knew better than to fight back. His friend Shinsho wasn't so wise.

'Master Tatsu! Stop! Please!' Shinsho cried.

Tatsu turned on Shinsho with every ounce of his explosive power. He caught Shinsho unprepared with a roundhouse kick that sent him flying across the room, slamming him into the wall. His limp body slipped to the floor. He lay still, dead.

Danny didn't move. He thought of Shredder, remembering how he had talked about 'family'. He thought about his own family, his mother, his father. He thought that he had a lot more thinking to do.

15

April took Casey and the Turtles to a farm in upstate New York that belonged to her family. It was far away from the city. April thought it would be a good place for them to hide. Raphael would have a chance to get well. They'd have time to make a plan to beat The Foot and save Splinter.

There were just a few problems in their way, though. Casey was a good mechanic and could fix anything. That was a good thing because many things at the farm were broken, including April's van. But it seemed that the thing Casey was the best at was hurting people's feelings and calling them names, like the way he told April about the message Charles had left on her machine right before they escaped.

'This is a good news/bad news situation,' Casey said. 'The bad news is that the car is broken because the block's got a crack in it about the size of the San Andreas fault, so you'd have to walk four miles to the neighbour's to call Charles and tell him you're taking some time off. The good news is that you don't have to make the trip. Charles called you. I heard him leave a message on your machine. You got fired!'

April thought Casey was the most insensitive man she'd ever met.

The Turtles had spent their entire lives living, learning, and working together. They had always been an inseparable quartet. The beating they'd taken at the hand of The Foot seemed to end all that.

Raphael, critically injured by The Foot, spent his days in a bath half filled with water. His pulse was weak, his breathing tortured, and, worst of all for a turtle, his shell was soft. He was alive, but just barely.

Leonardo almost never moved from Raphael's side. There was nothing he could do for his brother, but being with Raphael was like being by himself. That was what he wanted.

Michaelangelo trained. He spent all his time in the barn, working on his ninja skills. He concentrated so hard on the skills of battle to death that it seemed he'd forgotten about life.

Donatello spent his days next to Casey, trying to repair things around the farm. They fixed an old truck, they unclogged the well, and they patched up the roof. They also chatted constantly.

'No way, atomic mouth,' Donatello said.

'Barfaroni.'

'Camel breath.'

'Dome head.'

'Elf lips.'

'Gack face!'

'Hose brain!!'

They could repair anything but the way they treated each other.

April, too, spent time alone. She found a diary she'd begun when she was a little girl and started writing again. In spite of the fact that Charles had fired her, she *was* a reporter. She wrote about what she saw going on around her with her friends – and Casey. She drew pictures of each of the Turtles. She liked what she drew.

The first ray of hope came when the Turtles had been at the farm for four days. Raphael woke up. He lifted his head a few inches.

'Hey,' he whispered to Leo.

Leonardo leapt up, almost too excited to speak. 'Raph! You're awake! How do you feel?'

'What's a guy got to do to get some food around here?'

Leo dashed to the doorway and yelled. 'Hey! He's awake. Bring some food!' He returned to his brother. With ninja speed, food arrived. So did April and Donatello.

April watched the reunion. It was a chance for Leonardo to apologize for teasing Raphael. Apologies weren't easy for anybody, but with the Turtles, it seemed as though it wasn't necessary. It was important and it was touching, but there was something missing.

Later, April wrote in her diary: 'The Turtles are four once again. And yet they're still not whole. But I think I understand. A lingering doubt remains – an unknown that they can't bear to face – their greatest fear.'

Later, in the darkness of the country night, Michaelangelo sat on the roof of April's barn, thinking.

He was glad that he and his brothers were alive. He was glad that they were safe. He was glad that April was

with them. But something was missing. Something big.

Without even realizing it, Michaelangelo stood up and reached for the sky with both hands. He cried loudly into the pitch-black night, '*Splinter!!!!!*'

Everyone at the farm heard him. Everyone felt the same desperation. Michaelangelo had spoken it for them.

The following day, Leonardo left the bathroom for the first time. He went to a field to meditate as Splinter had taught them. He concentrated.

Hundreds of miles away, in a warehouse filled with hate and destruction, Splinter lifted his head and whispered a single word, 'Leonardo.'

At that instant, Leonardo knew. He ran back to the farm. He was almost out of breath when he arrived at the porch, where his brothers were drinking lemonade with April and Casey.

'He's *alive*!' Leo told them. 'Splinter's *alive*!'

The others thought maybe the whole situation was just getting to be too much for Leo. Yet – could it be?

16

That night, Leo took his brothers to the woods to meditate. They lit a fire and sat around.

'Leo, if you dragged us out here for nothing . . . ' Raphael began.

'Don't worry,' Donatello told Raph, pulling out a bag of marshmallows. 'I came prepared.'

'Put those away,' Leonardo said. 'Now, just do what I told you. Everybody close their eyes and concentrate. Concentrate hard.'

They did. And when they were all concentrating together on the same thing, it seemed as if the flames of the fire changed. It took some time, but when it was done, it was unmistakable. There, in the middle of their campfire, stood the image of their master, Splinter. He spoke:

'I am proud of you, my sons. Tonight you have learned the final and greatest truth of the ninja, that ultimate mastery comes not of the body, but of the *mind*. Together, there is nothing your four minds cannot accomplish. Help each other. Draw upon one another.'

The image began to fade, but Splinter continued talking. 'And always remember the true force that binds you, the same as that which brought me here tonight. That which I gladly return with my final words: I love you all, my students . . . my sons . . . my family.'

Splinter's image disappeared. His final word echoed in the woods. 'Family.'

Four Turtles sat around the fire, the same as they had been just a few minutes before, but very different, too. They were no longer four individuals. They were one team.

They began their real work together early the next morning.

Everything was different, everything was better. The Turtles found skills they never would have imagined they had.

'Hey, look!' Leo said. He turned his mask around so it was a blindfold and drew his katana from its sheath. 'OK, now attack me. All three of you. At once.'

His brothers looked at him as if he'd lost his shell. 'Give me a break, Leo,' Raph said.

'You'll get hurt!' Don told him, truly concerned.

'Come on!' Leo said, tapping Raph on the shoulder with the side of the blade to egg him on.

'Knock it off, Leo. That hurt!' Raph said.

Leo tapped him again, harder. It was enough to ignite Raphael's short fuse. He drew his sai and attacked. Leo defended himself, knocking the sai out of Raph's hands without hurting him at all. It was as if Leo could see right through the material. But he couldn't. They all knew that.

Then all three attacked. Leo used his newfound skills to repel the attacks, quickly disarming all of his

brothers. When his work was done, he turned his mask around again and smiled triumphantly.

His brothers were impressed. '*Rad*ical!' Michael-angelo said.

'I think you're going to have to teach us this one,' Donatello said.

'Splinter did the teaching,' Leo said. 'I'll just show you how.'

It was the ultimate weapon – the sixth sense. It was mind over matter, and the Turtles trained to be able to use it in concert with all their other weapons. They trained hard.

It took time to hone their skills, but as they worked they learned, and as they learned, they became even more united.

April and Casey couldn't believe the change in their friends. It was unity and it was love. It was so dramatic that Casey and April couldn't help being affected by it themselves. Their own anger seemed to dissolve. Their bickering stopped. Their friendship began.

A few days later, April and Casey were sitting on the farmhouse porch, relaxing and chatting. Four Turtles suddenly appeared before them. They looked very different from the four Turtles who had arrived at the farm a few short weeks earlier. These four were healthy, strong, confident. Once again they were the indomitable Teenage Mutant Ninja Turtles.

Leonardo spoke for them all.

'It's time to go back.'

17

It was a mess, but it was home and the Turtles were glad to be there. The Turtles, April, and Casey were tired after their long drive from the farm. Casey didn't seem to like the den very much, though.

'Great. Just great. First it's the Farm That Time Forgot, and now this. Why don't I ever fall in with people who own condos?' April gave him a nasty look. He didn't get the hint. 'I guess it's hard to get good maid service in a sewer. Maybe you should try Roto-Rooter.' Casey thought that was pretty funny. Nobody else did.

'Quit complaining,' April said, 'it's just for a little while.'

'Boy, I'm hungry,' Michaelangelo said. He looked at the kitchen cabinets. 'I wonder if there's anything—'

There was something, but it wasn't something to eat. There was a strange, loud noise from the cabinet. Don and Mike drew their weapons and each took a handle of the cabinet. On a signal, they tugged the doors open and out tumbled—

'Danny Pennington?' April said, very surprised. Danny had the oddest way of turning up at the most unlikely times.

Danny's arms flew up as soon as he spotted the ninja weapons. 'Don't shoot!' he said, terrified.

'I don't think it's loaded, kid,' Raphael said, teasing a little.

Danny crawled out of the cabinet. He told April that he'd run away from home and found this hiding place. April tried to get him to call his father. She knew how worried Charles would be.

'No, please!' Danny begged. 'Can't I spend the night with you guys? I'll call him in the morning. I *promise*.'

'Well . . . ' Finally she agreed.

The friends settled into the den for a restful evening and a good night's sleep. April told Danny where they'd been and some of what had been happening. She showed him the sketches she'd made of the Turtles.

'Boy, these are *good*!' he said. She was pleased. 'You think maybe I could have one?'

April couldn't resist his admiration. 'Sure,' she said. She gave him a sketch of the Turtles training with masks. He folded it carefully and put it in his pocket.

'Man, I could really go for a little deep-dish action right about now,' Michaelangelo said.

'Well, I had some pizza down here the other day. There might be some left over,' Danny told him. He pointed to a pizza box on the counter.

Carefully, Don lifted the cardboard lid and peered inside.

'Well?' Michaelangelo asked.

'Depends,' Donatello said.

'On what?'

'On if you like penicillin on your pizza.'

They went to bed hungry. The Turtles needed a good night's sleep. Tomorrow would be a busy day. Tomorrow they would find Splinter and they would free him.

Casey couldn't sleep in the cramped den. He decided, instead, to sleep in the truck, which was parked above the den on the city's deserted street.

Casey was awakened in the dead of the night by the sound of a manhole being pushed aside. He opened his eyes and watched. It was Danny!

Danny walked quickly and quietly along the street, and when he was about a half block away, he began jogging. Casey slipped out of the cab of the truck and followed Danny. He ran silently.

Danny ran downtown and then across a bridge to Brooklyn. Casey kept up with him. Finally Danny slowed down. He arrived at a huge warehouse. He circled it until he got to a small door on one side. Danny paused outside the door. He stuck his hand in his pocket and pulled something out. It was a headband. He tied it around his head, opened the door, and entered.

Casey didn't have any idea what was up, but he knew this was no time to stop and think. Fearlessly he reached for the door and entered the headquarters of The Foot.

He couldn't believe what he saw!

18

anny walked quickly through the training areas and into the remote storage section. There he found the rat.

'I have not seen you for many days,' Splinter said. He sounded weak. Danny was a little concerned.

'I've been at my hideout a lot.'

'And so you hide from your surrogate family as well as your own now . . . '

Danny shrugged. He was so confused. Splinter continued talking. 'I, too, once had a family, Daniel.' Danny looked at Splinter. He knew Splinter was about to tell him a story from his own life. He hoped it would help him understand and decide.

'I was a pet, belonging to Master Yoshi. I learned the mysterious art of Ninjitsu by copying his moves while I was in my cage. Yoshi was one of the finest shadow warriors of his clan. His only rival was a man named Oroku Nagi.'

While Danny listened intently, Splinter told him how Yoshi and Nagi had been in love with the same woman. Her name was Tang Shen. Tang Shen didn't love Nagi, though. She loved Splinter's master, Yoshi. When Nagi heard about that, he flew into a rage and beat Tang Shen.

'Yoshi arrived just in time to save Tang Shen, but when the fight was over, Nagi lay dead.' Danny knew how serious it was if members of a clan killed one another. 'The clan's code of honour was clear: Yoshi must now take his own life. But my master felt he had done nothing wrong, and so decided to flee with Tang Shen and me to America.'

Danny was fascinated to listen to Splinter's story. What a life the rat had led!

'Nagi was dead,' Splinter continued. 'But he left behind a younger brother, Oroku Saki. Saki promised the clan to track down my master. He trained with hatred and became the most feared ninja warrior in all Japan. He turned the clan from one of honour to one of death and thievery without honour. When he was ready to fulfil his vow, he, too, came to America.'

Splinter spoke more quietly now. 'I remember when my master returned home to find his beloved Shen had been murdered. Then he saw her killer. Saki wasted no words. He attacked Yoshi right away with his katana. When he swung it for the first time, he knocked my cage on the floor and it broke. I leapt to the man's face, biting and clawing! But he threw me back to the floor and took one swipe with the sword. In an instant, half my ear was gone. But that wasn't the worst of it. With the same swipe, he killed Master Yoshi.'

Danny felt Splinter's deep sadness at the loss.

'Whatever happened to this Saki guy?' Danny asked.

'No one really knows,' Splinter said. Then he looked deeply into Danny's eyes. 'But you wear his symbol upon your brow.'

Without thinking, Danny reached up and felt the headband he'd just put on. Saki and Shredder?

Well, Danny thought. *I was right about one thing. Splinter's story sure has helped me decide some things about the course of my own life.*

He took off his headband and dropped it on to the floor, for good.

19

Then Danny heard the thunderous voice that he now feared and hated most.

'What are you doing in there, boy?' Shredder asked.

'Oh, nothing,' Danny said. He tried to sound as innocent as possible. It didn't work. Shredder didn't believe him. Almost as if he knew where he'd find something, Shredder went into Danny's pocket. Tatsu watched while Shredder pulled a carefully folded piece of paper from Danny's pocket. He opened it slowly. It was April's drawing of the Turtles. Shredder paled.

He knew what it meant. 'They're back,' he said. Then his eyes seemed to light with the fire of hatred. 'There will be no mistakes this time!' he told Tatsu. 'I go myself.' He started for the door and then spoke one more time. 'Tatsu, the rat has served its purpose. We don't need it any more. Kill it.'

Then Shredder was gone.

Danny needed help to save Splinter, but he didn't know where to get it. As fast as he could, he ran from

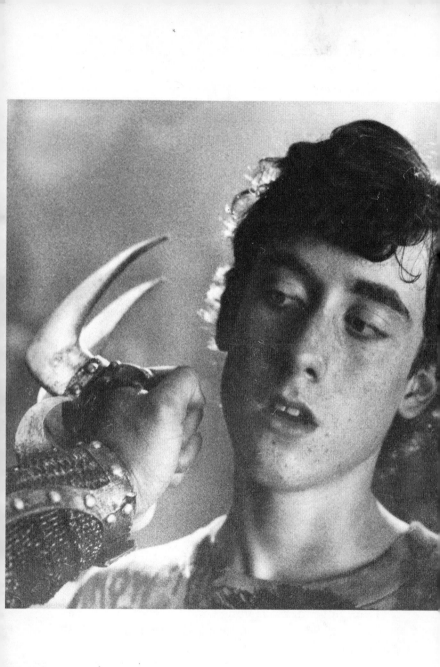

the room, searching for a friend, an ally. Everywhere he looked, The Foot were running for the door, ready to follow Shredder into battle. Where could Danny get help?

'Oooooomph!' he said as he stumbled and fell down. He looked to see what had happened. He'd been tripped by someone in a dogi and ninja mask. 'What are you doing?' Danny demanded.

The boy who had tripped him yanked off his mask. It was Casey! 'You've got some serious explaining to do!' Casey said.

This was the help Danny needed. 'You've got to come with me! They're going to kill Splinter!'

Danny didn't have to say it twice. Casey and Danny dashed back into the secluded section of the warehouse together.

Across the river, the battle began. When the Turtles and April discovered that both Danny and Casey were gone, they smelled a rat and it wasn't Splinter. They knew, somehow, they were about to be attacked. They prepared for it.

The first wave of The Foot arrived at the den and found nothing. They stood in the living room, totally confused. When a full battalion had gathered, the Turtles attacked with a full head of steam — literally.

Donatello blasted the entire bunch with a load of steam from an overhead pipe. They were completely overcome and fell down.

'Gosh, I do hope there are more of them,' Raphael said. Casually he took a bite out of an apple.

As if on cue, the second wave arrived. 'Ah, good.' Raphael welcomed them. It was time for Turtle Power!

*　　*　　*

Back in the warehouse, Casey followed Danny to Splinter's prison area. Casey had never met Splinter. He was surprised to see such a big rat. He was also surprised to see such a weak rat. 'Where do they . . . ?' he began, but he didn't have to finish the sentence. Danny tossed him the set of keys that hung by the entrance.

'Who are you?' Splinter asked, surprising Casey once again.

'Name's Casey Jones,' he said. 'I'm—' Casey didn't know how to explain. 'I'm a friend,' he said. It was the first time in a long time he'd used that word. Casey had forgotten what friendship was until the Turtles had taught him. This was no time for philosophy, though. He finished unlocking Splinter. 'OK, let's get out of here!'

But suddenly Tatsu was between them and the exit.

Casey was tough, but Tatsu was tougher. His ninja skills far outmatched Casey's primitive punches and kicks. Casey tried to talk tough, but that didn't work any better than his fighting.

Tatsu punched. Casey staggered backwards into shelves filled with stolen clothes. Tatsu kicked. Casey flew against boxes of stolen electronics. Tatsu chopped. Casey stumbled on to a pile of stolen jewellery. Tatsu sliced. Casey slammed. This time, though, he hit something familiar. It was stolen sporting equipment. He had his back up against a golf bag! Casey had an idea. With his last ounce of strength, he pulled a golf driver out of the bag. In the nick of time, he made the tee-shot of his lifetime. He swung back and then through!

═══ 78 ═══

'Fore!' he yelled. He whacked Tatsu in the stomach. Tatsu crashed to the floor, out cold.

'I'll never call golf a dull game again!' Casey promised. He kissed the club head.

'We've got to go!' Danny said. But as he helped Splinter towards the door, the room began to fill up with his fellow recruits and first-level trainees.

Once again, things weren't looking too good, until Danny realized that, like him, these guys had seen what Tatsu had done to Shinsho. *Maybe there was another way*, he thought.

20

The Turtles had never fought more fiercely. The Turtles had never fought better. And the Turtles had never had more fun!

'Gangway!' Donatello hollered. He rode his skateboard through the sewer, making S-curves and knocking out Foot Clan warriors with his bo as he scooted along the mucky hallway.

'Show-off!' Raphael yelled. He was just waiting for his chance. Fortunately there were enough enemy warriors to give him lots of opportunities.

The Turtles stacked them up like cord wood, pushing the bad guys out of their den through the sewer passageways and popping them up on to the street.

Don and Mike fought back-to-back, each protecting the other's flank. One of The Foot decided to attack them both at once, from their rears. The Turtles simply moved closer to one another, squeezing the helpless Foot warrior with their shells. Mike glanced over his shoulder at the fallen fighter. 'Looks like this one's suffering from "shell shock",' he said.

Don tried not to laugh. He couldn't help himself. It felt too good.

'I guess we can really "shell it out",' Donatello suggested. Mike laughed at the same time as he fended off six more attackers with his nunchukus.

'You guys have got it all wrong,' Raph said. 'It was a "shell" of a good hit!' His swirling sai took out three Foot Clan as he spoke.

'Aw right!' Mike said, finishing off the last of his half-dozen attackers.

Once the den and the sewer entrance were cleared of Foot, the Turtles began chasing the guys on to the street. Leonardo and Raphael chased some stragglers up a fire escape.

Mike joined in on the fun, but he was so busy chasing that he didn't notice he was being followed until he heard the grunt of a ninja thrust. He turned around just in time to see a razor-sharp katana aimed at his neck. He did the only logical thing. He pulled his head into his shell! The surprised attacker lost his balance and tumbled on to the street.

'I *love* being a Turtle!' Mike said. All of them felt exactly the same way. It was positively exhilarating.

Within a very short time the roof was nearly cleared of Foot Clan. Suddenly there was a hushed silence among their attackers. Those who were still standing stopped fighting and stood aside. Then the Turtles got their first look at their real enemy. It was Shredder.

'Anybody have any idea who – or *what* – this is?' Leo asked his brothers.

'I don't know,' Michaelangelo said, looking at Shredder's bladed armour, which was sparkling in the morning sun. 'But I bet he never has to look for a tin opener.'

Shredder ignored the humour. 'You fight well. In the old style,' he said. 'But you've caused me enough trouble. Now you face – the Shredder!' He stood like a king waiting for his courtiers to bow.

'The Shredder?' Donatello asked. It sounded very weird to him.

Michaelangelo shrugged. 'Maybe all that hardware's for making coleslaw.' Nobody laughed.

Shredder twirled his six-foot-long bo and set himself for battle.

'*I've* got him,' Raphael claimed. Shredder knocked him flat in less than two seconds.

The Turtles attacked, one at a time, but they couldn't beat Shredder that way. They'd never seen anyone anything like him. One-on-one was out of the question no matter how many wisecracks they made.

The Turtles were too busy working on a strategy to beat Shredder to notice what was happening below. Casey, Danny, and Splinter arrived, bringing with them new allies. All the recruits who had seen Tatsu's attack on a member of his own family were now ready to join up with the Turtles to defeat Shredder – if it could be done.

'OK, guys, *team*work,' Leonardo reminded his buddies. They didn't need a reminder. They attacked as one. And Shredder repelled them as one. He knocked them on their shells, slapping them away like so many gnats.

Mike rubbed his head and turned to his brothers. 'Now, at exactly what point did we lose control here?' he asked.

Donatello shrugged. 'Maybe somebody ought to tell him that *we're* the good guys.'

Raphael turned to Leonardo. This was a time when they needed his leadership more than ever. 'Any thoughts?' Raph asked.

'Just one,' Leonardo said. 'That this guy knows where Splinter is.'

It was the thought they all needed to share. They prepared for a new, and tougher attack.

Meanwhile, down on the street, Casey noticed that there were a whole bunch of recovering Foot who were preparing to climb up the fire escape and join in the fray. The Turtles had it tough enough against Shredder. They didn't need any more enemies.

Casey spotted a rubbish truck parked near by. He hopped into the cab and backed the monstrous vehicle right up to the building, mashing the fire escape. All the ninja who were trying to climb up found themselves tumbling down.

'Welcome to Rubbish City, Humpty Dumpty,' Casey said proudly.

Up on the roof, Shredder had once again repelled the Turtles, but not before they drew blood. Shredder was surprised – and a little concerned.

'Where's Splinter?' Raphael asked. His voice was filled with quiet fury. His anger was controlled and focused.

Shredder smiled. It was a cruel smile. 'Oh, the rat, you mean. So it has a name – or, I should say, *had* a name.'

The implication sank in immediately. All of the Turtles' cool anger turned red-hot instantly. Leonardo couldn't control himself. He flew at Shredder in a rage.

Just as fast, Shredder disarmed him, threw him to the floor of the roof, and put his foot on him triumphantly. 'He dies!' he said as the other three prepared to attack.

They stopped instantly. 'Throw down your weapons, now!' he commanded, nodding towards the roof's edge.

Raphael, Donatello, and Michaelangelo tossed their weapons over the edge of the roof, believing it was the only way to save Leonardo's life.

Shredder laughed. 'Fools! The three of you might have overpowered me. Now your fate will be *his*!' He raised his bo to stab Leonardo through the heart. The Turtles gasped.

And then they heard the voice they thought they would never hear again.

'*Saki!*' Splinter called. All movement on the roof stopped.

21

Shredder took his foot off Leonardo and turned to face Splinter. The Turtles understood that Shredder's real enemy was Splinter. They also knew that Splinter and Shredder must now do battle – to the death.

'Yes, Oroku Saki,' Splinter said, using the warrior's Japanese name. 'I know who you are. We met many years ago, in the home of my master, Hamato Yoshi!'

Then Shredder realized who Splinter was and how Splinter and his Turtles had learned to fight so well.

'And now I will finish what I began with your ear,' Shredder said. When he growled, it sounded like the fiercest, angriest animal who had ever prowled. He ran straight at Splinter with his bo pointed towards the rat's heart.

Shredder never saw Splinter's nunchukus spin, he never saw them fly. He never saw them wrap around his bo, tightening with each whipping rotation. The power of the 'chuks swept Shredder right to the edge of the roof and took him flying into midair.

'Death comes for us all, Oroku Saki,' Splinter said calmly. 'But something much worse comes for you. For when *you* die,' he said, watching Shredder soar toward the street, 'it will be . . . ' Shredder's limp body landed noiselessly in the rubbish truck, 'without honour,' Splinter finished.

The jaws of the rubbish truck opened. Shredder was swallowed by them, joining all the other rubbish. They clamped shut. Shredder disappeared into the morass.

The remaining Foot Clan dropped their weapons in total submission to Splinter and the Turtles. The victors almost didn't notice, though. The Turtles were too busy hugging Splinter, and he was too busy hugging them back.

22

Within a few minutes the street was filled with police, ambulances, fire appliances, and even the Channel Three News van, which was carrying Charles Pennington.

Danny spotted his dad first. He knew he had a lot of work to do to make up for all the trouble he'd caused. He wanted to start right away. He hurried towards his father. But before he reached his father, he found April.

'Here,' he said, handing her twenty-three dollars.

'What's this for?' April said, confused.

'It's something I owe you,' he said. 'Trust me'.

April looked at the money. Then she remembered her wallet. She could still hear Danny's words, 'trust me'. For the first time in a long time, she thought she *could* trust him. She watched him hug his dad. That was going to be a story with a happy ending.

Then April watched as Chief Sterns rounded up the tattered remains of The Foot. She wished she could be a fly on the wall when Sterns had to admit to the world that she, April O'Neil, had been right! But April O'Neil wasn't a reporter any more. She'd been fired. Or had she? Within a few minutes, Charles was positively *begging* her to come back to work.

'But, April, I *told* you, there were circumstances. I *need* you to cover this!'

April walked away. He followed her. 'Well, I don't know, Charles. You know, May Williams over at Channel Five has her own *office*—'

'You can have an office.'

'She's also the highest paid field reporter in New York.'

Charles looked at the story going on around him with no reporter to tell it. He swallowed his pride. 'Now *you* are the highest paid in the city.'

'OK,' April said. 'Get me a mike.' She was back in business!

Splinter and the Turtles watched from the rooftop above.

'We were awesome,' Leonardo said.

'Bo-*da*-cious!' Michaelangelo added.

'Totally excellent!' Raphael said.

'A perfect ten,' said Donatello.

They looked to Splinter for his evaluation. 'I have always liked . . . ' He paused. They waited. 'Cowabunga!'

'Cowa-*bun*-ga!' they all said in unison. Then they gave one another the 'high threes' that their hands allowed.

Victory was sweet.

23

A few days later, April and Danny entered the offices of Mar-Cee Comics. They had an appointment with the publisher himself.

After a long wait in the reception area, a secretary ushered them into Mr Cushing's office. It was spacious and had huge picture windows all along one wall. The other walls were covered with comic-book covers featuring such weird creatures as Amazing Aardvarks, Mighty Marsupial, and Nuclear Nightwing. These were some of Danny's favourites. That's why they had chosen this particular company for April's proposal.

April handed Mr Cushing an envelope. He opened it and pulled out her drawings. They were the sketches she had made of the Turtles while they were training at the farm. Mr Cushing examined them carefully, but April couldn't help notice that his eyebrows kept popping up.

'Uh, these are, uh, very *interesting*, Miss O'Neil,' he said after a few minutes. 'But as the basis for a comic book? I'm afraid the idea is just too . . . '

He searched for a word. April and Danny waited.
'. . . uh, too far-fetched.'

Mr Cushing was very surprised to see that April and Danny were almost laughing when he said it.

He would have been even more surprised if he'd turned around right then. He would have seen four very far-fetched Teenage Mutant Ninja Turtles clinging to his picture window with suction cups, laughing hysterically.

THE END